# TOM LOGAN SERIES

# CATTLE CARS

By
**EDNA WALKER CHANDLER**

Illustrated by
**JACK MERRYWEATHER**

**BENEFIC PRESS**
**WESTCHESTER, ILLINOIS**

Library of Congress
Number 71-94908

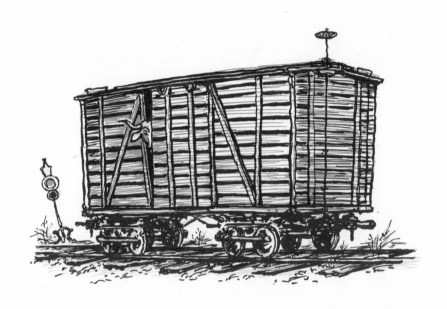

U.S. 1694176

# CONTENTS

# The Train Is Here

Tom Logan saw the cattle. There were hundreds of cattle going to market.

Tom was looking for the herd boss.

"Where is the herd boss?" he asked some men who were standing around talking.

"I am Jack Brown, boss of this herd," a man said. "I come from Laramie. I want to take my cattle to the market in Kansas City."

"I am Tom Logan, railroad boss," Tom said.

"The cattle train is here now, and it is ready to go."

"Can you get my cattle to market soon?" asked Jack Brown. "Can a train get cattle to market? I have driven cattle to market many times, but I have never put them on a train. A train is something new to me."

"Sure, we can get your cattle to market soon," said Tom. "After you put them on the train, you will not want to drive cattle again. The train will be much easier and faster. You will see."

"I hope I am doing the right thing," said Jack. He was worried about the train.

"O.K., said Jack. "I will call my men to help load the cattle."

Tom helped Jack Brown's men as they worked to get the cattle on the train. Jack Brown's men worked very hard. The cows and calves did not want to go on the train. They were afraid of the cars.

Jack Brown worked hard along with his men. He had to count the number of cows, calves, and steers which he was taking to the market in Kansas City.

Tiger was running here and there as the men worked to load the cattle. The cows and calves did not like Tiger. They were afraid of him. He kept barking at them.

Then Tom said, "Tiger, I will put you on the train. You cannot help load cattle. You are getting in the way. Here, come with me into this car."

As Tom closed the door, Jack Brown came to him.

"We are ready, Tom," he said. "The cattle are on the train. The doors are closed, and we are ready to begin the ride to Kansas City."

"Good for you and your men," said Tom. "You got the cattle on the train very fast. I will tell the rest of the men that we are ready to start for Kansas City."

"Tom," said Jack. "Can we get to Kansas City in two or three weeks?"

Tom laughed at Jack. "This is not a walking train," he said. "This train runs fast! If you were driving your cattle to Kansas City, it would take you many weeks to get there. It is a hard drive. But on the train your cattle will be in Kansas City in three or four days!"

"What?" said Jack. "You cannot get to Kansas City in three or four days. No one can do that."

"Oh yes," said Tom. "This train can do that. Just wait and see."

14

Tom Logan told the engine man to start the train moving.

The long train pulled out of the station.

The train went slow at first. Then it went faster and faster.

Tom Logan looked at Jack Brown.

"We are on the way to Kansas City with your cattle," he said. "Your cattle are going to market on a good, fast train. They will get to market soon. When they get there, they will still be fat cattle. You will not want to drive cattle over the land to market again."

# Trouble For a Train

The train went faster and faster. It went up hills and down hills. There were big mountains it had to climb. It went through forests as it went over the land on its way to Kansas City.

Now and then the train had to make a stop at cattle pens. Jack Brown had to feed his cattle. He had to give them water, too. He wanted his cattle to be fatter than the cattle which had been driven over the land.

When the cattle were through eating, Tom Logan helped Jack Brown load the cattle again, and the train went on its way.

The train went on when night came. Jack Brown, his cowboys, and Tom went to sleep. Tiger slept near Tom.

The engine man kept the train going over the land. Then he went to sleep, and another man kept the train running. All day and all night the train went on and on.

While the men slept and the man kept the
train running, it began to rain. The rain began
to come down harder and harder. The train
began to go slower. It went slower and slower.
Then it stopped!

The wind went "oo! oooooo!" And the rain
came down harder and harder.

Tom woke up. So did Jack Brown. All of the men woke up, too.

"What is the trouble?" Jack Brown asked Tom. "It looks like the train has stopped."

"You're right," said Tom. "I will see what the trouble is. Wait here. I will talk to the engine man."

Tom went away to talk to the engine man. He was not gone long. Then he came back to the men.

"We cannot go now," Tom said to the men. "The rain is coming down too hard. The engine man says that he cannot see the tracks."

"What will we do?" asked Jack. "We must get going again soon."

"The rain will stop soon," said Tom. "It looks clearer now."

"There is nothing to do but to wait for the rain to stop," said the men.

Tom and Jack saw that the cattle did not like the rain. They were moving around in the cars and making noises.

Tiger did not like the rain. He was sitting close to Tom.

Jack Brown was worried.

"I must get my cattle to market soon," he said to his men. "My friends told me that the train is not a good way to go. But I did not think that they were right. I wanted to go this way. I do not like long cattle drives."

Jack looked at Tom.

"My friends are walking their cattle to market," he said. "They will get there first. Then they will laugh at me."

Tom heard what Jack Brown was saying.
"Your friends will not get to market first,"
Tom answered. "This train will go again soon.
The train will get you and your cattle to market
in two more days. You will get your cattle to
market first, Jack. You will see."

At last the rain stopped. The wind stopped, too. By now it was morning. The men were up and moving about. The train went on. It could run now that the rain had stopped.

"I am glad the rain has stopped now," said Tom. Tom wanted to get to Kansas City as much as Jack Brown did.

Tom got some things
to eat.

"Who wants to eat?"
he asked the men.

"We all want to eat!"
said Jack and his men.

All of the men sat
down and began to eat.

Tiger was hungry,
too. He ate as the men
ate! Tiger was happy!

Jack Brown was happy, too. The train was on its way to Kansas City again. All was well now. Jack Brown and his men were very happy. They sang as the train moved along over the tracks.

The men began to talk about what they would do when they got to Kansas City.

"I have some friends there," said one of the men. "They have asked me to come to their house when I get to Kansas City. Some of you may come along with me if you want to."

"That would be fun," said some of the men. "We would like to go along."

The men talked some more as the train moved along.

Suddenly, the train stopped.

Toot! Toot! The train stopped still on the tracks. It did not move.

"Now what is the trouble?" Jack Brown asked. "We just get going along and the train stops again. What a train! What a ride! Will we get the cattle to Kansas City this way?"

One of the engine men came to Tom.

"Tom," he said, "We have trouble again. A big tree is on the track. The wind put it there. We will have to get the tree off the track before this train can go again."

"O.K.," said Tom. "We will need all the help
we can get. Come on men! Let's go! We will
get that tree off the track."

Jack Brown looked worried again. "What
if we don't get the tree off the track?" he asked.

"Don't worry, Jack," said Tom. "I know we
can do it. But all of you must help."

"Let's get started then," said Jack. "Let's
hope we can move that big tree before it is
too late."

The men got to the tree. It was across the
tracks, and it was very big.

"Put your ropes around the tree," said Tom.

The men put their ropes around the tree.

"Now, pull!" Tom called. "Pull as hard as
you can, men!"

The men pulled as hard as they could. But the tree did not move.

"Come on, men. Pull harder!" called Tom again. "We must move the tree!"

The men pulled and pulled. Still the tree did not move.

"We will not move
the tree this way," said
Tom. "The tree is too
big. There are not
enough of us to move
it off the tracks."

Tom looked a little worried. He looked at the men.

"What can we do, men?" he asked. "How can we move this tree?"

"Maybe we can put more ropes on the tree and pull harder," said one of the men.

"I don't think that will work," said Tom. "The tree is just too big for us to move."

"There is nothing we can do, now," said Jack
Brown. "We will not get the cattle to Kansas
City. There is nothing to do but to drive the
cattle across the land. The train will not work.
I should have done as my friends did."

Jack Brown walked to the cattle car.

"Come on, men," he said. "Let's get the cattle out of here and start driving them to Kansas City. We can still make it if we hurry!"

"Wait," said Tom. "I think I know what we can do. I still think we can move that tree off the tracks."

The men watched as Tom went to talk to the engine man.

"Can the engine move that tree?" Tom asked the engine man.

"I don't know," the man said. "The engine has many cars to pull, and the cars are full of cattle. I don't know if the engine can move the tree or not. We can try, Tom."

"Could we take the engine off the train?" Tom asked. "The rest of us can put rocks on the tracks. Then the cattle cars cannot go, but the engine can. Then the engine can move the tree off the track."

The engine man was thinking. Tom hoped that he would say yes to his idea.

"Yes, I think that your idea will work," said the engine man. "We will take the engine away from the cattle cars. We will try it. Tell your men what to do. Then we will try to move the tree."

Tom told the men what to do. They put
rocks on the tracks so that the cattle cars
would not move down the track. All of the
men worked hard. Jack Brown worked hard,
too. He wanted to get to Kansas City fast.

Tiger ran here and there as the men worked.

"Here, Tiger," Tom called. "You can help, too." Tom put a rock in Tiger's mouth. "Take it to the tracks, Tiger," Tom said.

Tiger took the rock to the tracks and put it down with the rocks the men had put there. The men laughed at Tiger.

"There," said Tom. "That should keep the cars from running away while we try to move the tree."

"It has to work," said Jack Brown. "It is getting late. I must get these cattle to market very soon."

"Let's take the engine off now," said Tom to the others.

"Don't worry, Jack. I'm sure this plan will work."

Tom and Jack and some men helped take the
engine from the cattle cars. It was hard work
to get the engine from the cattle cars, but soon
the men were able to do it.

Then Tom went to the engine man. He said,
"Now you can get the engine away from the
cattle cars."

The engine man made the engine go. He
was moving the engine to the tree.

The engine pushed the tree. It pushed harder and harder against the tree. The tree began to move, but it did not move off the track. The engine man made the engine go back. Then he pushed the engine against the tree again. This time the tree moved off the track. The track was clear now!

"Hoorah!" the men called. "Hoorah for the engine man! Hoorah for Tom Logan! His plan worked! The engine man moved the tree! Now the train can go again."

"Hoorah for you men, too!" called Tom. "You helped to move the tree!"

44

# Where Is the Engine?

The men got on the train.

"We're on our way again," said Jack. Jack was not worried now. The train was moving over the land.

On and on went the train. In one or two more days the train would get to Kansas City. Then Jack Brown and his men would be happy. Tom Logan would be happy, too.

Tom looked out at the land.  He did not see big hills.  He did not see big rivers.

"We will soon be in Kansas City," said Tom. "Kansas City is a good cattle market."

"Yes," said Jack Brown.  "We are getting near the market now."

"Soon your cattle will be at the market," said Tom.  "They are fat, too.  They will bring a good price."

The train was running well. The men were
happy. They were talking to each other and
laughing loudly.

Then suddenly the train stopped again.
There was a loud noise.

The men stopped talking at once. Each one
looked at the other. Jack Brown could not say
a word. Another worried look came on his face.

"What is that noise?" asked Tom. He ran to the car door, and looked out.

"What!" Tom yelled. "We have no engine!"

"No engine!" yelled Jack Brown. "Where is it?"

"We must stop the cattle cars!" Tom yelled. "They are going down that hill. We must stop them before they do. If they go down the hill fast, they will run off the track."

"What can we do?" asked Jack Brown. "Tell us what to do and we will do it! The cattle must get to market."

"They will not get to market if this train does not stop soon," said some of the men.

Tom was thinking fast.

"Come on, Jack. I need your help!" Tom called out. Jack came close to Tom.

"The cars are going slow now," Tom said. "Now we have to stop them before they begin to go faster. Help me!"

Jack helped Tom get to the top of the car. Tom wanted to stop the train cars with the brake on top.

Tom got to the top of the car. He turned the brake. Jack looked on as Tom worked to stop the train. The train was getting close to the hill now. The men below were not talking now. They were not laughing.

The cattle were making noises. They were afraid, too.

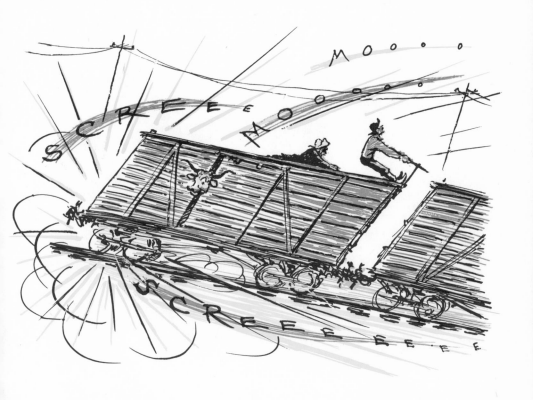

Tom turned the brake. The train began to slow down. Then it stopped. It stopped before it got to the top of the hill.

"We stopped! We stopped!" called all the men. "Tom stopped the train!"

"The cattle are safe," said Jack.

"We are all safe," said Tom. "But it was a close one!"

Tom looked up the track. He could see that the engine had stopped, too.

The engine man had stopped the engine. Now he was making the engine go back to the cars on the track.

"Now we will soon go again," said Tom. The engine was coming back to the cars slowly. The men walked to the engine as it came up the track.

"The engine is ok," said the engine man. "The train will go again."

The men looked at the engine. They did not
see the cattle cars. There was more trouble
in the cattle cars. Tom did not see the trouble.
The men were laughing and talking about the
runaway engine. They did not know that they
had more trouble.

Tiger saw the trouble. "Bow-wow! Bow-wow!" said Tiger. He wanted Tom and the men to know about the trouble. But Tom and the men did not hear Tiger. They were talking to the engine man. They did not think there could be more trouble.

# Runaway Cattle

Tom saw Tiger. He saw Tiger running near the cattle cars. Tom saw the car door open.

"Look!" he yelled. "The cattle are coming out of the train. They are running away from the train. Hurry! They are running fast. We must get them!"

Tom ran to shut the door. Jack Brown ran with him.

Tom and Jack could not get near the door. The cattle were coming out too fast for them to try to shut the door.

"We cannot shut this door!" said Jack. "The steers will run over us. We must keep the other car doors shut."

"You are right, Jack," said Tom. "Come on, men, help us keep the other doors shut!"

Now Jack Brown was very worried. He looked at Tom.

"You cannot run a cattle train," he said. "Now I know my friends were right. It is better to drive cattle to market. It may be harder, but it is the best way."

Tom felt bad. He had told Jack that he would get his cattle safely to Kansas City and that he would get him there faster than he could drive them over land.

"I am sorry, Jack," said Tom. "I am very sorry. We are having a lot of trouble. I didn't think we would have so much trouble. But we will still get to market on time. We will do it. You will see."

"We have had trouble all the way!" said Jack. "I will not take my cattle on a train again. We will go on the long trail."

"We must get help," said Tom. He looked far away. "There is a ranch over there," he said. "Maybe we can get some help there."

Tom and Jack started running to the ranch. As they went, they told the other men to watch the cattle.

"We will go for help," Tom and Jack said. "You men had better watch the cattle. They will look for water. Try to see where they go. We will be back soon."

Tom and Jack ran faster. They knew they had to get help fast.

"I see somebody," yelled Tom. "Let's hope he has some horses and will help us."

"He had better help us," said Jack. "If not, we have more trouble than we can take!"

Tom and Jack could see that the rancher was working with some calves.

"Good morning, Mister," said Tom. "I am Tom Logan. I am running a cattle train to Kansas City, and we have run into some trouble. This is Jack Brown, boss of the herd."

"Glad to meet you," said the rancher. "Now, what is your trouble?"

"One of our cattle car doors opened," said Tom. "The cattle are coming out of the car too fast."

"We are afraid that we will lose the cattle," said Jack. "I must get them to market. And soon it will be too late."

"Can you help us?" asked Tom. "We need all the help we can get."

"Sure, we will help," the rancher said. "The men at the Flying D are good cowboys. I have two men here. The other men are out with my herd."

"We have four men," Tom said. "We have no horses. Can you let us use some of your horses? We need them."

"Sure," said the rancher. "I have men with horses. I have horses for your men. Come on, let's go!"

Tom and Jack helped get the horses. Then
the rancher went with Tom and Jack. Two of
the rancher's cowboys went on horses.

Tom and Jack were on horses and had three
other horses with them.

Tom, the rancher, and the cowboys all went
back to the train.

The cattle were running away from the train.
"You do have trouble," said the rancher.
"But I think we can help you out of it."
Jack Brown looked worried.

Tom could see that Jack was worried again.
"Don't worry, Jack," Tom said. "We will get the cattle back on the train and be on our way again."

The cattle were running here and there.

"You go that way," Tom yelled to some men. "And you go the other way," he said to Jack and some other men. "We will close in on them. Then we can take them back to the cattle car."

The cowboys did as Tom said. They worked around the cattle and got them together. It was hard work. The cattle were afraid. They did not know where they were. But the cowboys had done this many times before. They knew what they were doing. It was hard work, too. The rancher and the cowboys did their best to get the cattle back into the car.

At last the cattle were back in the car.

Jack Brown was counting the cattle to make sure they were all back.

Suddenly, Jack Brown looked worried again.

"They are not all here," said Jack. "One of my cows is not here."

"We will look again," said one of Jack Brown's men.

"I don't think you need us now," the rancher said to Tom.

"I want to thank you and your men for all your help," said Tom. "We would not have been able to get the cattle back into the car without you. Thank you, again."

"Maybe we can help you some day," said Jack to the rancher.

"That's ok," the rancher answered. "I am sure that there will be other people in trouble which you will be able to help."

"You're right," said Tom. "And I sure will do that!"

The rancher and his men went back to their ranch. They were glad they had helped.

# One Very Little Cow

The train was ready to go again. Jack Brown said, "One of my men went to look for a cow. One cow is not here, and she is one of my good ones."

"We will wait here," said Tom. "That cow did not go far. Your man will get her. Then we will put her back on the train with the other cattle."

Soon the man who had gone after the cow came back. He was riding the rancher's horse. He had the cow.

"The cow was over near the ranch," the cowboy said to the men. "There were some cattle there. Maybe the cow wanted to make some new friends."

The cowboys laughed. Then they saw something on the cowboy's horse.

Tom looked at Jack Brown. Jack looked back at Tom. Then they laughed.

"Looks like you have one more calf in your herd, Jack," Tom said.

"What can we do with it?" Jack asked. "We cannot put it in the cattle car."

"Wait!" Tom said. He ran into the car where the men were sitting.

Soon he came out.

"We will put the cow and calf in here," Tom said. "I have a place ready for them."

"O.K.," said Jack. "That is a good idea. The cow and calf will be safe in there. We can watch them."

Tom told the engine man to go back. The
train started backing up to get the cow. When
the train got back to the cow, Tom took the
little calf. He went into the car with the calf.
He looked back at the cow.

The cow was not coming into the car. The cow was afraid to go into the car. The cow looked at Tom.

"Moo! Moo!" the cow was saying.

"Come," said Tom. "Here is your calf. Come here."

Then the cow started moving into the car. The cow was not afraid now.

"You are good with cows," said Jack. "You are better with cows than you are with trains!" he said.

All the cowboys laughed.

Tom went to get some food and water for the cow. Soon he came back with it.

"I know that this cow is hungry," Tom said. "She has been away from feed."

"That's right," said Jack. "I want the cow to be fat for market."

Tom gave the food and the water to the cow. Then he looked at the little calf.

"This is a fine calf," he said. "It will make a fine cow some day. Maybe some day we will take this calf on this train to market," Tom said to Jack.

"We will see if we get these cattle here to market first!" laughed Jack.

"Are we ready to start again?" asked the engine man.

"Yes, we are ready," Tom answered. "The cow is in the car, and the calf is there, too. We are ready to go."

"I hope this is the last of our troubles," said Jack. "I did not know so much could happen on one train ride!"

"Yes, we have had our troubles for one train ride," said Tom. "But all is well now."

Jack Brown looked at the cow. Then he looked at the calf. It was a fine calf. And the cow was doing well, too.

"We did have one good thing happen on this train ride, Tom," Jack Brown said. "We have one more cow than we started with. It is a fine calf, too. And we can take the calf with us without much trouble. On a long drive over land, it would be hard to take the calf with us. We would have to find some other place to put the calf. Maybe trains are good for something after all!"

"Yes," said Tom. "This train will take the calf right along to market in Kansas City. The calf could not walk a long way. And it would be hard for a man to take it on a horse on a long drive."

Jack and Tom were tired. They had worked very hard for the last two days.

The men were tired, too. Getting the cattle back into the cars was hard work. Now, they could rest.

The train started on its way again. It went
on and on.

"One more day and one more night," said
Tom. "Then we will be in Kansas City."

"One more day and one more night if there
is no more trouble," said Jack.

"There won't be more trouble," said Tom. "What could happen that has not happened?" Tom laughed.

"I think you're right," said Jack. "Nothing could happen now!"

The train went on as the men talked.

Time went by fast. Soon the men saw Kansas City. It was a big city. They saw the cattle pens, too. They saw hundreds and hundreds of cattle in the pens. There were lots of people around the cattle. They wanted to see which ones would be the best to buy.

"Look at all those pens!" Jack said. "What a big market!"

"I am glad we got your cattle here this soon," said Tom.

"Yes," said Jack. "We will be able to get them into the pens soon."

There were other trains coming to the market in Kansas City.

There were lots of cowboys in the market. There were lots of horses, too. The cows were making noises.

"Moo! Moo!" they said.

Tiger did not like the cattle market. He was afraid of all the noises.

The men looked at all the pens. It was a very big market.

"There is a herd walking to market," said Tom to Jack.

"They do not look very fat," said Jack. "They do not look very good at all."

"And they look very tired," Tom said.

"The bosses look just as tired," said Jack Brown. "I'm not tired at all now."

"See?" said Tom. "That herd walked a long way. The cows are not fat. The men are very tired. Your cattle are fat. And your cowboys did not get tired. Soon all ranchers will put their cattle on the trains. There will be no more long cattle drives, Jack!"

"You may be right, Tom," Jack Brown said slowly. "You may be right."

At last the train stopped. Then the men got the cattle out of the train and put them in the pens.

"The train came through, Jack," said Tom. "I knew we could do it. And your cattle look better than most of the other herds."

"That's right!" said Jack and his men. "The cattle train was a good idea after all. And maybe next time we won't have as much trouble," Jack said.

"Right," said Tom. "Now, let's get something to eat. I know we are all hungry. You and your men will be well rested by the time your friends get here," said Tom.

# VOCABULARY

The total number of different words in this book is 296. The 51 words in roman type would be familiar to children reading at second-grade level. The 17 words in italics are above second-grade level. The rest of the words used in the book are below second-grade level. The number after each word indicates the the page on which it first appears.

*able*   42
against   43
answered   24

bad   60
begin   13
below   52

calf   76
cannot   12
*cattle*   7
*clearer*   22
*cowboys*   18

done   36
drive   9
*driven*   8

*easier*   9
engine   15

faster   9
fatter   17
felt   60
forests   16

happen   83
harder   19
*herd*   7

hope   9
hundreds   7

*idea*   37
I'm   41

kept   12

land   15
late   31
load   11
*lose*   66
lot   61
loud   47

market   7
maybe   62
meet   65
mountains   16

number   11

*pens*   17
plan   41
pushed   43

*railroad*   8
*ranch*   62

rocks   37
ropes   32

safe   53
shut   58
slept   19
slower   19
slowly   55
*somebody*   64
sorry   61
station   15
suddenly   29
sure   9

those   88
tracks   22
*trail*   61
trouble   16

we're   45
without   72
woke   20
won't   85
*worry*   31

*yelled*   48
*you're*   20